CITY B

AN URBAN BIRDWATCHING LOGBOOK
ILLUSTRATIONS BY CHRISTINE BERRIE

LAURENCE KING PUBLISHING

[01] **AFRICAN PARADISE FLYCATCHER**
[02] **AMERICAN ROBIN**
[03] **BARN OWL**
[04] **BLACK REDSTART**
[05] **BLUE JAY**
[06] **BLUE TIT**
[07] **BOHEMIAN WAXWING**
[08] **BULLFINCH**
[09] **CAMPO FLICKER**

[10] **CANADA GOOSE**
[11] **CHINESE POND HERON**
[12] **COMMON (EURASIAN) BLACKBIRD**
[13] **COMMON CUCKOO**
[14] **COMMON (EURASIAN) JAY**
[15] **COMMON KINGFISHER**
[16] **COMMON (EURASIAN) SWIFT**
[17] **EURASIAN SPARROWHAWK**
[18] **EUROPEAN BEE-EATER**

[19] **EUROPEAN GOLDFINCH**
[20] **EUROPEAN ROBIN**
[21] **EUROPEAN STARLING**
[22] **GOLDEN ORIOLE**
[23] **GREAT HORNED OWL**
[24] **GREAT SPOTTED WOODPECKER**
[25] **GREY HERON**
[26] **HAMERKOP**
[27] **HERRING GULL**

[26]

[27]

[28]

[29]

[30]

[31]

[32]

[33]

[34]

[35]

[36]

[37]

[38]

[39]

[40]

[41]

[42]

[43]

[44]

[45]

[46]

[47]

[48]

[49]

[50]

[28] **HOOPOE**
[29] **HOUSE MARTIN**
[30] **HOUSE SPARROW**
[31] **JACKDAW**
[32] **LAUGHING KOOKABURRA**
[33] **MAGNIFICENT FRIGATEBIRD**
[34] **MAGPIE**
[35] **MALLARD**
[36] **MONK PARAKEET**

[37] **MUTE SWAN**
[38] **NORTHERN CARDINAL**
[39] **ORIENTAL WHITE-EYE**
[40] **PEREGRINE FALCON**
[41] **PIED (WHITE) WAGTAIL**
[42] **RAINBOW LORIKEET**
[43] **RED-WHISKERED BULBUL**
[44] **RUBY-THROATED HUMMINGBIRD**
[45] **SERIN**

[46] **SULPHUR-CRESTED COCKATOO**
[47] **SUPERB FAIRYWREN**
[48] **SUPERB STARLING**
[49] **WHITE-BREASTED KINGFISHER**
[50] **WOODPIGEON**

[01]

AFRICAN PARADISE FLYCATCHER
Terpsiphone viridis

Small, with black crest, blue eye-ring, chestnut upperparts and, in the male, extravagant tail streamers. Darts out from perch to capture insects in flight. Builds tiny cup-shaped nest, from which male's long tail dangles while sitting.

LENGTH	28–35 cm	11–13¾ in
WINGSPAN	±25 cm	9¾ in
WEIGHT	12–14 g	up to ½ oz

DISTRIBUTION Sub-Saharan Africa and southern Arabian Peninsula; savannah woodland and open forest, including parks and gardens.

TIME & DATE

LOCATION

BEHAVIOUR

FEMALE-MALE

WEATHER

OTHER

[02]

AMERICAN ROBIN

Turdus migratorius

Medium-sized thrush. Named for red-orange breast, which resembles that of European robin. Very common and widespread. Feeds on insects, fruit and berries, often foraging on lawns. Known for blue eggs and complex song. Northern populations migrate south in winter.

LENGTH	23–28 cm	9–11 in
WINGSPAN	31–41 cm	12–16 in
WEIGHT	72–94 g	$2\frac{1}{2}$–$3\frac{1}{4}$ oz

DISTRIBUTION Across North America; most habitats, including residential areas.

TIME & DATE

LOCATION

BEHAVIOUR

FEMALE-MALE

WEATHER

OTHER

[03]

BARN OWL
Tyto alba

Pure white underparts and heart-shaped face. Hunts rodents at dusk or after dark using powerful hearing and agile, silent flight. Often nests in old buildings. Spectral appearance and eerie, hissing calls have inspired ghost stories.

LENGTH	33–39 cm	13–15$\frac{1}{4}$ in	DISTRIBUTION All continents except
WINGSPAN	80–95 cm	31$\frac{1}{2}$–37$\frac{1}{2}$ in	Antarctica; open country, often
WEIGHT	250–500 g	8$\frac{3}{4}$–17$\frac{1}{2}$ oz	around farms.

TIME & DATE

LOCATION

BEHAVIOUR

FEMALE-MALE

WEATHER

OTHER

[04]

BLACK REDSTART

Phoenicurus ochruros

Robin-sized, with upright stance, black face and red, constantly quivering, tail. Feeds on insects and nests in cavities. Common around buildings, often perching on roofs. Tinkling song ends with strange crunching gravel sound.

LENGTH 13–14.5 cm 5–5¾ in
WINGSPAN 23–26 cm 9–10¼ in
WEIGHT 14–20 g ½–¾ oz

DISTRIBUTION South and central Europe (rare in UK), east to China; cliffs, coastal and residential areas, including urban and industrial.

TIME & DATE

LOCATION

BEHAVIOUR

FEMALE-MALE

WEATHER

OTHER

[05]

BLUE JAY

Cyanocitta cristata

Blue and white with blue crest and black collar. Readily visits garden
feeders. Intelligent, like other members of crow family: mimics
the calls of raptors, collects shiny objects and may bury food to
collect later.

LENGTH	22–30 cm	$8\frac{3}{4}$–12 in
WINGSPAN	34–43 cm	$13\frac{1}{2}$–17 in
WEIGHT	70–100 g	$2\frac{1}{2}$–$3\frac{1}{2}$ oz

DISTRIBUTION North America, mostly
east of the Rockies; woodland and
residential areas.

TIME & DATE

LOCATION

BEHAVIOUR

FEMALE-MALE

WEATHER

OTHER

[06]

BLUE TIT

Cyanistes caeruleus

Small, colourful and acrobatic. Often feeds upside down and commonly visits garden bird feeders. Nests in tree holes and takes readily to nest boxes. One pair may collect 10,000 caterpillars for their nestlings in three weeks.

LENGTH	11.5 cm	4½ in	
WINGSPAN	18 cm	7 in	
WEIGHT	11 g	½ oz	

DISTRIBUTION Common across Europe, including Britain; woodland, parks and gardens.

TIME & DATE

LOCATION

BEHAVIOUR

FEMALE-MALE

WEATHER

OTHER

[07]

BOHEMIAN WAXWING
Bombycilla garrulus

Starling-sized, with crest. Breeds in northern forests; migrates south in winter, sometimes visiting the UK. Gets its name from the red, wax-like tips to its secondary wing feathers. Flocks to ornamental berry bushes in towns.

LENGTH   19–23 cm $7\frac{1}{2}$–9 in
WINGSPAN   32–35 cm $12\frac{1}{2}$–$13\frac{3}{4}$ in
WEIGHT   45–70 g $1\frac{1}{2}$–$2\frac{1}{2}$ oz

DISTRIBUTION Northern Eurasia and North America; irregular winter visitor to the UK.

TIME & DATE

LOCATION

BEHAVIOUR

FEMALE-MALE

WEATHER

OTHER

BULLFINCH

Pyrrhula pyrrhula

Plump, with thick bill and rose-pink underparts in male (female browner). Feeds on buds and is unpopular in some regions for damaging orchards. Shy, generally sticking to cover, but will visit garden feeders.

LENGTH	15.5–17 cm	6–6¾ in	
WINGSPAN	22–29 cm	8¾–11½ in	
WEIGHT	27–38 g	1–1¼ oz	

DISTRIBUTION Europe and Asia east to Japan; declining in the UK; mixed woodland and gardens with dense cover.

TIME & DATE

LOCATION

BEHAVIOUR

FEMALE-MALE

WEATHER

OTHER

[09]

CAMPO FLICKER

Colaptes campestris

Ground-feeding woodpecker with black, yellow and red face and head. Often feeds in small groups, hopping about in search of termites, ants and beetles. May hammer holes in termite mounds. Nests in tree holes.

LENGTH   28–31 cm   11–12¼ in
WINGSPAN   42–51 cm   16½–20 in
WEIGHT   145–192 g   5–6¾ oz

DISTRIBUTION Eastern South America, from central Brazil to central Argentina; open country, savanna and pampas.

TIME & DATE

LOCATION

BEHAVIOUR

FEMALE-MALE

WEATHER

OTHER

[10]

CANADA GOOSE

Branta canadensis

Large, long-necked goose with black and white head. Races vary in size. Feeds on grass and grain. Has colonized residential areas across its range. Feral populations thrive in parks and towns across Europe. Flocks migrate in V formation.

LENGTH 75–110 cm 30–43 in
WINGSPAN 127–185 cm 50–73 in
WEIGHT 2.6–6.5 kg $5\frac{3}{4}$–$14\frac{1}{4}$ lb

DISTRIBUTION Widespread across North America; introduced to Europe and New Zealand.

TIME & DATE

LOCATION

BEHAVIOUR

FEMALE-MALE

WEATHER

OTHER

[11]

CHINESE POND HERON

Ardeola bacchus

Small, compact heron. Inconspicuous when perched but reveals striking white wings in flight. Feeds at the water's edge, alone or in small, scattered groups. Snatches fish, frogs and invertebrates with dagger bill.

LENGTH	47 cm	18½ in
WINGSPAN	75–90 cm	9¾–11 in
WEIGHT	370 g	13 oz

DISTRIBUTION China and eastern Asia, migrating further south in winter; ponds, ditches and freshwater wetlands, including in urban areas.

TIME & DATE

LOCATION

BEHAVIOUR

FEMALE-MALE

WEATHER

OTHER

[12]

COMMON (EURASIAN) BLACKBIRD
Turdus merula

Male black; female brown. Very common and widespread. Often feeds on lawns, cocking head to listen for earthworms underground. Sings rich, melodious song from rooftops and high perches. Belongs to thrush family; unrelated to American blackbirds.

LENGTH	24–26 cm	$9\frac{1}{2}$–$11\frac{1}{2}$ in	DISTRIBUTION Europe, Asia and North
WINGSPAN	35–38 cm	$13\frac{3}{4}$–15 in	Africa; woods, parks and gardens.
WEIGHT	80–125 g	$2\frac{3}{4}$–$4\frac{1}{2}$ oz	

TIME & DATE

LOCATION

BEHAVIOUR

FEMALE-MALE

WEATHER

OTHER

[13]

COMMON CUCKOO
Cuculus canorus

Hawk-shaped, with long tail. Named for male's loud two-note call.
Summer visitor to Europe from Africa. Eats hairy caterpillars. Lays
eggs in nests of 'host' birds, such as meadow pipit, which raise cuckoo
nestling as their own.

LENGTH	32–36 cm	12½–14¼ in	DISTRIBUTION Summer migrant to Europe
WINGSPAN	55–60 cm	21½–23½ in	and Asia; winters in Africa;
WEIGHT	110–130 g	4–4½ oz	declining in the UK.

TIME & DATE

LOCATION

BEHAVIOUR

FEMALE-MALE

WEATHER

OTHER

[14]

COMMON (EURASIAN) JAY
Garrulus glandarius

Small, pinkish-grey member of crow family, with black, white and blue markings. Sticks to cover, where presence often betrayed by harsh call. Wide diet includes acorns: caches up to 5,000 every autumn as winter food supply.

LENGTH	35 cm	14 in	DISTRIBUTION Across Eurasia;
WINGSPAN	52–58 cm	21–23 in	widespread in deciduous woodland,
WEIGHT	140–190 g	5–6¾ oz	including in urban areas.

TIME & DATE

LOCATION

BEHAVIOUR

FEMALE-MALE

WEATHER

OTHER

[15]

COMMON KINGFISHER

Alcedo atthis

Vivid colours, dagger-shaped beak and fast, direct flight. Always found beside water. Dives beak-first to catch small fish, usually from regular perch. Excavates nesting tunnel in riverbank. Enters built-up areas along canals.

LENGTH	16–17 cm	$6\frac{1}{4}$–$6\frac{3}{4}$ in	DISTRIBUTION Europe and southern Asia;
WINGSPAN	25 cm	$9\frac{3}{4}$ in	widespread in the UK, but absent
WEIGHT	34–46 g	$1\frac{1}{4}$–$1\frac{1}{2}$ oz	from far north and Ireland.

TIME & DATE

LOCATION

BEHAVIOUR

FEMALE-MALE

WEATHER

OTHER

[16]

COMMON (EURASIAN) SWIFT

Apus apus

Resembles all-dark swallow with long, scythe-shaped wings. Aerial insect eater. Feeds and sleeps on the wing, landing only at its nest – a mud and saliva construction on cliffs and buildings. Groups race above towns in summer, making screaming calls.

LENGTH	16–18 cm	7 in
WINGSPAN	42–48 cm	17–19 in
WEIGHT	36–50 g	1–1¾ oz

DISTRIBUTION Breeds in Eurasia and winters in sub-Saharan Africa; feeds over all habitats, including in towns.

TIME & DATE

LOCATION

BEHAVIOUR

FEMALE - MALE

WEATHER

OTHER

EURASIAN SPARROWHAWK

Accipiter nisus

Small raptor with short broad wings and long tail. Male grey above with orange barring below; female brown and 25 per cent larger. Specialist woodland predator of small flying birds, often raiding gardens and bird feeders for its prey. Widespread but elusive.

LENGTH	28–40 cm	11–16 in
WINGSPAN	60–80 cm	24–32 in
WEIGHT	150–320 g	5–11 oz

DISTRIBUTION Eurasia, with some populations wintering in southern Asia and north Africa; widespread in wooded areas, including towns.

TIME & DATE

LOCATION

BEHAVIOUR

FEMALE - MALE

WEATHER

OTHER

[18]

EUROPEAN BEE-EATER

Merops apiaster

Dazzling plumage, pointed tail and agile, floating flight. Hunts from
perch, capturing bees and other insects in mid-air. Can eat 250 bees
a day. Colonies nest in sand banks, each pair digging its own tunnel.

LENGTH	27–29 cm	10–11½ in	DISTRIBUTION Breeds in Mediterranean
WINGSPAN	36–40 cm	14–15¾ in	Europe and east/central Asia;
WEIGHT	44–78 g	1½–2¾ oz	migrates in winter to Africa and
			southern Asia; open country.

TIME & DATE

LOCATION

BEHAVIOUR

FEMALE-MALE

WEATHER

OTHER

[19]

EUROPEAN GOLDFINCH

Carduelis carduelis

Small and colourful; gold wing bars flash in flight. Extracts seeds
from thistles using sharp bill. Often visits hanging feeders.
Once popular as cage bird for its tinkling song. Common motif in
Renaissance art, associated with the Madonna and Child.

LENGTH	12–13 cm	$4\frac{3}{4}$–5 in	DISTRIBUTION Europe and western Asia;
WINGSPAN	21–25 cm	$8\frac{1}{4}$–$9\frac{3}{4}$ in	open country, parks and gardens.
WEIGHT	14–19 g	$\frac{1}{2}$–$\frac{3}{4}$ oz	

TIME & DATE

LOCATION

BEHAVIOUR

FEMALE-MALE

WEATHER

OTHER

[20]

EUROPEAN ROBIN

Erithacus rubecula

Bright orange breast, bold demeanour and delicate song. Often feeds
around gardeners, taking insects from soil. Association with Christmas
stems from Victorian postmen, who wore red and were nicknamed 'Robin'.
Belongs to flycatcher family; unrelated to American robin.

LENGTH	12.5–14 cm	5–5$\frac{1}{2}$ in	DISTRIBUTION Europe, Western Asia and
WINGSPAN	20–22 cm	8–8$\frac{3}{4}$ in	North Africa; common in the UK.
WEIGHT	16–22 g	$\frac{1}{2}$–$\frac{3}{4}$ oz	

TIME & DATE

LOCATION

BEHAVIOUR

FEMALE-MALE

WEATHER

OTHER

[21]

EUROPEAN STARLING

Sturnus vulgaris

Iridescent black plumage and sharp bill. Common in towns. Nests in holes and mimics other birds in its inventive song. Highly sociable; outside breeding season may roost in huge flocks that perform spectacular aerial displays. Destructive invader where introduced.

LENGTH	19–23 cm	7½–9 in
WINGSPAN	31–44 cm	12¼–17¼ in
WEIGHT	58–101 g	2–3½ oz

DISTRIBUTION Native to Europe and western Asia; introduced to North America, Australia and South Africa; open habitats and built-up areas.

TIME & DATE

LOCATION

BEHAVIOUR

FEMALE-MALE

WEATHER

OTHER

[22]

GOLDEN ORIOLE
Oriolus oriolus

Thrush-sized, fruit-eating songbird with fluting call. Male brilliant yellow and black; female leaf green. Shy; usually glimpsed flitting between trees. Summer visitor from Africa. 'Oriole' derives from Latin *aureolas*, meaning 'golden'.

LENGTH	22–25 cm	$8\frac{1}{2}$–$9\frac{3}{4}$ in
WINGSPAN	46 cm	18 in
WEIGHT	60–80 g	$2\frac{1}{4}$–$2\frac{3}{4}$ oz

DISTRIBUTION Breeds from southern and central Europe to Central Asia; winters in sub-Saharan Africa; open woodland, orchards and plantations.

TIME & DATE

LOCATION

BEHAVIOUR

FEMALE-MALE

WEATHER

OTHER

[23]

GREAT HORNED OWL
Bubo virginianus

Big and fierce-looking, with cryptic plumage and prominent ear tufts.
Commonest large owl in the Americas. Hunts by night for variety of
prey, from insects to jackrabbits. Grip of talons five times stronger
than human hand.

LENGTH	43–64 cm	17–25 in
WINGSPAN	91–153 cm	3–5 ft
WEIGHT	1.2–2.5 kg	$2\frac{1}{2}$–$5\frac{1}{2}$ lb

DISTRIBUTION North, Central and South
America, from Alaskan sub-Arctic to
Argentinian pampas; most habitats,
including residential areas.

TIME & DATE

LOCATION

BEHAVIOUR

FEMALE-MALE

WEATHER

OTHER

[24]

GREAT SPOTTED WOODPECKER

Dendrocopos major

Black and white, with red under tail and on head of male and juvenile.
Climbs tree trunks with tail braced against bark. Uses powerful bill
to extract grubs from wood. Hammers loudly on dead branch during
'drumming' courtship display. Often visits feeders.

LENGTH $\quad$ 22–23 cm $\quad$ $8\frac{3}{4}$–9 in $\quad$ DISTRIBUTION Across Eurasia;
WINGSPAN $\quad$ 34–39 cm $\quad$ $13\frac{1}{2}$ –$15\frac{1}{2}$ in $\quad$ widespread in woodlands, parks
WEIGHT $\quad$ 70–90 g $\quad$ $2\frac{1}{2}$ –$3\frac{1}{4}$ oz $\quad$ and wooded gardens.

TIME & DATE

LOCATION

BEHAVIOUR

FEMALE-MALE

WEATHER

OTHER

[25]

GREY HERON

Ardea cinerea

Tall, with long legs and neck. Found near water, often wading deep.
Hunts aquatic prey such as fish and frogs, standing motionless before
seizing victim in dagger bill. Roast heron was once a prized dish for
European nobility.

LENGTH	84–102 cm	33–40 in	
WINGSPAN	155–195 cm	61–76$\frac{3}{4}$ in	
WEIGHT	1–2 kg	2$\frac{1}{4}$–4$\frac{1}{2}$ lb	

DISTRIBUTION Europe, Africa and Asia;
aquatic habitats inland or on coast,
including in built-up areas.

TIME & DATE

LOCATION

BEHAVIOUR

FEMALE - MALE

WEATHER

OTHER

[26]

HAMERKOP

Scopus umbretta

Brown, heron-like water bird in family of its own. Crested head has hammer-like shape, hence Afrikaans name. Enormous domed nest is often used by other birds, including geese and owls. Feared as evil omen in some African cultures.

LENGTH	56 cm	22 in	DISTRIBUTION Sub-Saharan Africa and
WINGSPAN	90–94 cm	35½–37 in	southern Arabian Peninsula; common
WEIGHT	415–430 g	14½–15 oz	around most wetlands and water
			bodies, including in built-up areas.

TIME & DATE

LOCATION

BEHAVIOUR

FEMALE-MALE

WEATHER

OTHER

[27]

HERRING GULL

Larus argentatus

Large, with grey back and yellow bill: the typical 'seagull'. Common
in some coastal towns, where it nests on buildings and scavenges from
waste. Uses at least 24 different calls. Some scientists classify
American herring gull as a separate species.

LENGTH	55–67 cm	21½–26 in
WINGSPAN	125–155 cm	49–61 in
WEIGHT	0.7–1.5 kg	1½–3¼ lb

DISTRIBUTION Britain, northwest Europe
and North America; rocky coasts and
coastal towns, sometimes inland
during winter.

TIME & DATE

LOCATION

BEHAVIOUR

FEMALE-MALE

WEATHER

OTHER

HOOPOE

Upupa epops

Long crest, striking colours and thin, curved bill. In floppy,
undulating flight resembles large moth. Nests in tree holes and probes
for food in ground, often lawns. Named for repetitive 'hoop hoop hoop'
call, given with crest fanned.

LENGTH   25–32 cm $9\frac{3}{4}$–$12\frac{1}{2}$ in   DISTRIBUTION Southern Europe, Asia,
WINGSPAN   44–48 cm $17\frac{1}{4}$–19 in   north and sub-Saharan Africa;
WEIGHT   46–89 g $1\frac{1}{2}$–$3\frac{1}{4}$ oz   variety of open habitats, including
                                    parks and farmland.

TIME & DATE

LOCATION

BEHAVIOUR

FEMALE - MALE

WEATHER

OTHER

[29]

HOUSE MARTIN
Delichon urbicum

Resembles small swallow, with shorter forked tail and white rump.
Summer visitor to Europe from Africa. Catches insects in agile flight.
Breeds around human habitation, building mud nests under eaves; may
use nest boxes.

LENGTH	13 cm	5 in	DISTRIBUTION Breeds in Europe and
WINGSPAN	26–29 cm	$10\frac{1}{4}$–$11\frac{1}{2}$ in	central Asia; winters in sub-
WEIGHT	18.3 g	$\frac{3}{4}$ oz	Saharan Africa.

TIME & DATE

LOCATION

BEHAVIOUR

FEMALE-MALE

WEATHER

OTHER

[30]

HOUSE SPARROW
Passer domesticus

Small and compact. Thrives around towns and human habitation. Uses
thick bill to feed on seed and spilled grain. Originally from Middle
East, but has since spread (via ships) to every continent
except Antarctica.

LENGTH	16 cm	$6\frac{1}{4}$ in	
WINGSPAN	21–25 cm	$8\frac{1}{4}$–$9\frac{3}{4}$ in	
WEIGHT	24–32 g	$\frac{3}{4}$–1 oz	

DISTRIBUTION The most widespread bird
in the world – Europe, Asia, Africa
Americas, Australasia; towns and
farmland.

TIME & DATE

LOCATION

BEHAVIOUR

FEMALE-MALE

WEATHER

OTHER

[31]

JACKDAW
Corvus monedula

Small, compact crow, with black plumage and grey nape. Acrobatic and vocal in flight. Common in towns. Nests in holes and sometimes chimney pots. Sociable: often flocks with other birds. Can mimic human speech. Features widely in folklore.

LENGTH	33 cm	13 in	DISTRIBUTION	Europe, Asia and North
WINGSPAN	67–74 cm	27–30 in		Africa; widespread, especially
WEIGHT	220–270 g	8–9 oz		on cliffs, coasts and urban areas.

TIME & DATE

LOCATION

BEHAVIOUR

FEMALE-MALE

WEATHER

OTHER

[32]

LAUGHING KOOKABURRA
Dacelo novaeguineae

Crow-sized kingfisher with powerful bill. Named for its ear-splitting
territorial call, given at dawn and dusk, with several individuals
often joining a competitive chorus. Common in suburbia. Captures
reptiles, mice and other small prey from the ground.

LENGTH	39–42 cm	15–17 in	DISTRIBUTION Native to eastern
WINGSPAN	56–66 cm	22–25 in	Australia and introduced to
WEIGHT	310–480 g	11–17 oz	southwest; also New Guinea; open
			woodland, parks and suburbia.

TIME & DATE

LOCATION

BEHAVIOUR

FEMALE-MALE

WEATHER

OTHER

[33]

MAGNIFICENT FRIGATEBIRD
Fregata magnificens

Large, black seabird with very long wings and long forked tail. So lightweight, its plumage weighs more than its skeleton. Male inflates red throat sac during breeding display. Snatches fish from the ocean surface and pirates food from other birds.

LENGTH	89–114 cm	35–45 in
WINGSPAN	217–244 cm	85–96 in
WEIGHT	1.1–1.6 kg	$2\frac{1}{2}$–$3\frac{1}{2}$ lb

DISTRIBUTION Tropical Atlantic and Pacific coasts of Americas, from Florida to Brazil; commonly seen soaring over coastal cities.

TIME & DATE

LOCATION

BEHAVIOUR

FEMALE-MALE

WEATHER

OTHER

[34]

MAGPIE

Pica pica

Black-and-white plumage and long tail. Noisy, rattling call. Broad
diet includes eggs and nestlings. Belongs to crow family. Renowned
for curiosity and intelligence: can recognize itself in mirror. Some
scientists class American (black-billed) as a separate species.

LENGTH	44–46 cm	17¼–18 in
WINGSPAN	52–62 cm	20½–24½ in
WEIGHT	180–270 g	6¼–9½ oz

DISTRIBUTION Europe, Asia, North
America; common in towns and most
open habitats.

TIME & DATE	LOCATION

BEHAVIOUR	FEMALE-MALE

WEATHER	OTHER

MALLARD

Anas platyrhynchos

Large, ubiquitous duck. Colourful male has dark green head and yellow bill; female mottled brown. A dabbler: upends to feed on tiny aquatic plants and animals. Ancestor of most domestic ducks worldwide. Native across northern hemisphere; introduced elsewhere.

LENGTH	50–65 cm	20–26 in	
WINGSPAN	81–98 cm	32–39 in	
WEIGHT	0.7–1.6 kg	$1\frac{1}{2}$–$3\frac{1}{2}$ lb	

DISTRIBUTION Europe, Asia, North America, Australia, New Zealand; abundant in most aquatic habitats, including town ponds and lakes.

TIME & DATE

LOCATION

BEHAVIOUR

FEMALE-MALE

WEATHER

OTHER

MONK PARAKEET

Myiopsitta monachus

Starling-sized parrot, with long tail. Largely green and yellow,
revealing blue wings in flight. The only parrot that builds a stick
nest. Breeds colonially in treetops. Intelligent and sociable;
popular as a pet.

LENGTH	29 cm	11½ in	
WINGSPAN	48 cm	19 in	
WEIGHT	100 g	3½ oz	

DISTRIBUTION Subtropical South
America, notably Argentina and
Brazil; feral populations in Spain
and Florida; thrives in cities.

TIME & DATE

LOCATION

BEHAVIOUR

FEMALE-MALE

WEATHER

OTHER

[37]

MUTE SWAN
Cygnus olor

Huge white waterfowl with orange bill and long neck. Native to Eurasia;
introduced elsewhere. One of the world's heaviest flying birds. Largely
voiceless, but wing beats audible from afar. Defends nest aggressively.
Thrives around people. Historically associated with British monarch.

LENGTH	125–170 cm	49–67 in
WINGSPAN	200–240 cm	79–94 in
WEIGHT	8.5–14.3 kg	$18\frac{3}{4}$ –$31\frac{1}{2}$ lb

DISTRIBUTION Europe, Asia, Australia, and North America; widespread on lakes, rivers and wetlands, including in towns.

TIME & DATE

LOCATION

BEHAVIOUR

FEMALE-MALE

WEATHER

OTHER

[38]

NORTHERN CARDINAL
Cardinalis cardinalis

Thick bill and perky crest. Male mostly bright red; female browner.
Feeds on seeds, berries and insects, often visiting feeders. Males
chase away territorial rivals. Once prized as a cage bird for its
bright colours and lively song.

LENGTH	21–23.5 cm	$8\frac{1}{4}$–$9\frac{1}{4}$ in	DISTRIBUTION North America east of
WINGSPAN	25–31 cm	$9\frac{3}{4}$–$12\frac{1}{4}$ in	the Rockies, from southern Canada
WEIGHT	33.6–65 g	$1\frac{1}{4}$–$2\frac{1}{4}$ oz	to Mexico.

TIME & DATE

LOCATION

BEHAVIOUR

FEMALE-MALE

WEATHER

OTHER

[39]

ORIENTAL WHITE-EYE
Zosterops palpebrosus

Small and delicate-looking; white, green and yellow, with white ring around eye. Small groups forage in trees and bushes for nectar and small insects, calling constantly. Bathes in dew that gathers on leaves.

LENGTH	9.6 –11 cm	$3\frac{3}{4}$–$4\frac{1}{4}$ in	DISTRIBUTION South and southeast Asia, from Pakistan to Indonesia; woodland, scrub, parks and gardens.
WINGSPAN	±18 cm	7 in	
WEIGHT	5.6–11 g	up to $\frac{1}{2}$ oz	

TIME & DATE

LOCATION

BEHAVIOUR

FEMALE-MALE

WEATHER

OTHER

[40]

PEREGRINE FALCON
Falco peregrinus

Dashing raptor with black cap and anchor shape in flight. Fastest known bird, exceeding 250 kph (155 mph) in aerial pursuit of other birds. Nests on cliffs, especially along coasts. Adapts to urban environments, breeding on tall buildings. Wanders widely outside breeding season.

LENGTH	36–49 cm	14–19 in
WINGSPAN	100–110 cm	39–43 in
WEIGHT	530–1,600 g	19–57 oz

DISTRIBUTION Every continent except Antarctica; hunts over most habitats; now breeds in London, New York and other major cities.

TIME & DATE

LOCATION

BEHAVIOUR

FEMALE-MALE

WEATHER

OTHER

[41]

PIED (WHITE) WAGTAIL
Motacilla alba

Small, with black-and-white plumage. Constant wagging of long tail is
thought to signal vigilance to predators. Forages energetically on
ground for insects, usually near water and often on pavements and in
car parks. May gather for warmth in large town-centre winter roosts.

LENGTH	18 cm	7 in	DISTRIBUTION Europe and Asia;
WINGSPAN	25–30 cm	9¾–12 in	widespread, including in towns.
WEIGHT	25 g	1 oz	

TIME & DATE

LOCATION

BEHAVIOUR

FEMALE-MALE

WEATHER

OTHER

[42]

RAINBOW LORIKEET

Trichoglossus moluccanus

Dove-sized parrot, with vivid colors and long tail. Feeds acrobatically in trees, using special brush-like tongue to extract nectar and pollen. Visits bird tables for fruit and seeds. May become tame enough to feed by hand.

LENGTH	25–30 cm	$9\frac{3}{4}$–$11\frac{3}{4}$ in	
WINGSPAN	45 cm	$17\frac{3}{4}$ in	
WEIGHT	75–157 g	$2\frac{3}{4}$–$5\frac{1}{2}$ oz	

DISTRIBUTION Australia's eastern seaboard, from northern Queensland to Tasmania; rainforest and coastal bush, common in suburbia.

TIME & DATE

LOCATION

BEHAVIOUR

FEMALE-MALE

WEATHER

OTHER

[43]

RED-WHISKERED BULBUL

Pycnonotus jocosus

Thrush-sized, with pointed black crest and red face patch. Eats fruits, nectar and insects. Common in parks and gardens, drawing attention with loud three-note call. Unwelcome non-native alien in some tropical regions around the world.

LENGTH	20–22 cm	8–8¾ in
WINGSPAN	25–28 cm	9¾–11 in
WEIGHT	23–42 g	¾–1½ oz

DISTRIBUTION Tropical south and southeast Asia; introduced to Hawaii and Australia; lightly wooded areas, including suburbia.

TIME & DATE

LOCATION

BEHAVIOUR

FEMALE-MALE

WEATHER

OTHER

[44]

RUBY-THROATED HUMMINGBIRD
Archilochus colubris

Tiny, with needle-like bill and metallic green upperparts. Only male
has red throat. Sips nectar from flowers while hovering. Visits garden
feeders. Beats wings at up to 75 times per second. Migrates 1,450 km
(900 miles) non-stop across Gulf of Mexico.

LENGTH	7–9 cm	$2\frac{3}{4}$–$3\frac{1}{2}$ in	
WINGSPAN	8–11 cm	$3\frac{1}{4}$ –$4\frac{1}{4}$ in	
WEIGHT	2–6 g	up to $\frac{1}{4}$ oz	

DISTRIBUTION Breeds in eastern North
America, from Mexico to southern
Canada; winters in Central
America; woods, parks and gardens.

TIME & DATE

LOCATION

BEHAVIOUR

FEMALE-MALE

WEATHER

OTHER

[45]

SERIN

Serinus serinus

Smallest European finch, closely related to canary. Male yellow; female browner. Stubby bill and forked tail. Feeds on seeds, buds and flowers, foraging near ground. Buzzing trill from treetop is a common spring sound around the Mediterranean.

LENGTH	11–12 cm	$4\frac{1}{4}$–$4\frac{3}{4}$ in
WINGSPAN	21–23.7 cm	$8\frac{1}{4}$–$9\frac{1}{4}$ in
WEIGHT	8.5–14 g	$\frac{1}{4}$–$\frac{1}{2}$ oz

DISTRIBUTION South and central Europe, east to Russia; winters in North Africa; parks, woodland edges, suburbia and gardens.

TIME & DATE

LOCATION

BEHAVIOUR

FEMALE-MALE

WEATHER

OTHER

[46]

SULPHUR-CRESTED COCKATOO
Cacatua galerita

Large white parrot with powerful bill and jaunty yellow crest. Raucous
call. Feeds on berries, nut and seeds, using tongue and toes to
manipulate food. May live over 70 years in captivity. Very intelligent:
can synchronize movements to a musical beat.

LENGTH	44–51 cm	$17\frac{1}{4}$–20 in
WINGSPAN	100 cm	39 in
WEIGHT	700–950 g	$1\frac{1}{2}$–2 lb

DISTRIBUTION Native to north and
eastern Australia and introduced
to southwest; open woodland,
parks, gardens and suburbia.

TIME & DATE

LOCATION

BEHAVIOUR

FEMALE-MALE

WEATHER

OTHER

[47]

SUPERB FAIRYWREN

Malurus cyaneus

Tiny, with perky tail. Breeding male has electric blue markings; female browner. Hops about on ground in search of insects. Male and female form pairs but each mates with multiple partners. Voted Australia's favourite bird in national poll.

LENGTH	14 cm	$5\frac{1}{2}$ in	
WINGSPAN	±22 cm	$8\frac{3}{4}$ in	
WEIGHT	8–13 g	$\frac{1}{4}-\frac{1}{2}$ oz	

DISTRIBUTION Southeastern Australia, from Queensland to Tasmania; woodland, heathland and suburbia – common in Sydney and Melbourne.

TIME & DATE

LOCATION

BEHAVIOUR

FEMALE-MALE

WEATHER

OTHER

[48]

SUPERB STARLING

Lamprotornis superbus

Iridescent blue/green upperparts contrast with red/orange belly.
Conspicuous white. Forages on ground for insects, fruits and seeds,
typically below acacia trees. Bold and noisy, often hopping around
picnic sites.

LENGTH   18–19 cm   7–7$\frac{1}{2}$ in

WINGSPAN   ±31 cm   12 in

WEIGHT   52–77 g   1$\frac{3}{4}$–2$\frac{3}{4}$ oz

DISTRIBUTION East Africa, from
Ethiopia to Tanzania; savannah and
open woodland, including in towns
and cultivated areas.

TIME & DATE

LOCATION

BEHAVIOUR

FEMALE - MALE

WEATHER

OTHER

WHITE-BREASTED KINGFISHER

Halcyon smyrnensis

Starling-sized, large bill, blue, white and chestnut plumage. Swoops down from branch or wire to capture frogs, reptiles, large insects and even other birds. Calls loudly during breeding season, often from buildings.

LENGTH	26–28 cm	10¼–11 in	DISTRIBUTION Southern Asia, from
WINGSPAN	40–43 cm	15¾–17 in	Turkey to China; open country,
WEIGHT	75–110 g	2½–4 oz	using wires and other perches, including in built-up areas.

TIME & DATE

LOCATION

BEHAVIOUR

FEMALE-MALE

WEATHER

OTHER

WOODPIGEON

Columba palumbas

Plump and pinkish-grey, with white collar. Largest UK pigeon. Very abundant. Feeds on seeds and drinks regularly. Gives nestlings 'crop milk', a rich fluid produced in crop (throat pouch) from semi-digested seed. Hunted for food and as an agricultural pest.

LENGTH	40–42 cm	15½ –16½ in	DISTRIBUTION Europe and parts of
WINGSPAN	75–80 cm	30–32 in	Middle East; common and
WEIGHT	450–550 g	1–1¼ lb	widespread, including woodland,
			farmland and urban areas.

TIME & DATE

LOCATION

BEHAVIOUR

FEMALE-MALE

WEATHER

OTHER

STICKER
LOG

[01]
AFRICAN PARADISE FLYCATCHER
Terpsiphone viridis

[02]
AMERICAN ROBIN
Turdus migratorius

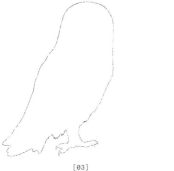

[03]
BARN OWL
Tyto alba

[04]
BLACK REDSTART
Phoenicurus ochruros

[05]
BLUE JAY
Cyanocitta cristata

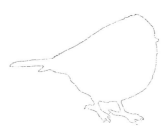

[06]
BLUE TIT
Cyanistes caeruleus

[07]
BOHEMIAN WAXWING
Bombycilla garrulus

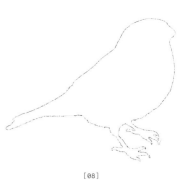

[08]
BULLFINCH
Pyrrhula pyrrhula

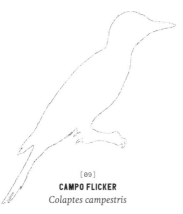

[09]
CAMPO FLICKER
Colaptes campestris

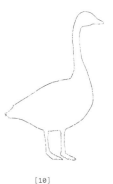

[10]
CANADA GOOSE
Branta canadensis

[11]
CHINESE POND HERON
Ardeola bacchus

[12]
COMMON (EURASIAN) BLACKBIRD
Turdus merula

[13]
COMMON CUCKOO
Cuculus canorus

[14]
COMMON (EURASIAN) JAY
Garrulus glandarius

[15]
COMMON KINGFISHER
Alcedo atthis

[16]
COMMON (EURASIAN) SWIFT
Apus apus

[17]
EURASIAN SPARROWHAWK
Accipiter nisus

[18]
EUROPEAN BEE-EATER
Merops apiaster

[19]
EUROPEAN GOLDFINCH
Carduelis carduelis

[20]
EUROPEAN ROBIN
Erithacus rubecula

[21]
EUROPEAN STARLING
Sturnus vulgaris

[22]
GOLDEN ORIOLE
Oriolus oriolus

[23]
GREAT HORNED OWL
Bubo virginianus

[24]
GREAT SPOTTED WOODPECKER
Dendrocopos major

[25]
GREY HERON
Ardea cinerea

[26]
HAMERKOP
Scopus umbretta

[27]
HERRING GULL
Larus argentatus

[28]
HOOPOE
Upupa epops

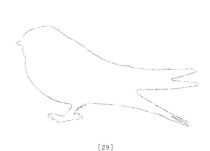

[29]
HOUSE MARTIN
Delichon urbicum

[30]
HOUSE SPARROW
Passer domesticus

[31]
JACKDAW
Corvus monedula

[32]
LAUGHING KOOKABURRA
Dacelo novaeguineae

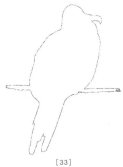

[33]
MAGNIFICENT FRIGATEBIRD
Fregata magnificens

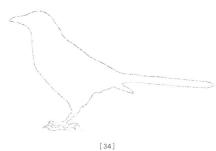

[34]
MAGPIE
Pica pica

[35]
MALLARD
Anas platyrhynchos

[36]
MONK PARAKEET
Myiopsitta monachus

[37]
MUTE SWAN
Cygnus olor

[38]
NORTHERN CARDINAL
Cardinalis cardinalis

[39]
ORIENTAL WHITE-EYE
Zosterops palpebrosus

[40]
PEREGRINE FALCON
Falco peregrinus

[41]
PIED (WHITE) WAGTAIL
Motacilla alba

[42]
RAINBOW LORIKEET
Trichoglossus moluccanus

[43]
RED-WHISKERED BULBUL
Pycnonotus jocosus

[44]
RUBY-THROATED HUMMINGBIRD
Archilochus colubris

[45]
SERIN
Serinus serinus

[46]
SULPHUR-CRESTED COCKATOO
Cacatua galerita

[47]
SUPERB FAIRYWREN
Malurus cyaneus

[48]
SUPERB STARLING
Lamprotornis superbus

[49]
WHITE-BREASTED KINGFISHER
Halcyon smyrnensis

[50]
WOODPIGEON
Columba palumbas

[01]

[02]

[03]

[07]

[05]

[06]

[04]

[08]

[09]

[10]

[11]

[13]

[12]

[14]

[16]

[15]

[17]

[18]

[19]

[21]

[20]

[22]

[23]

[24]

[25]

[26]

[28]

[30]

[29]

[27]

[32]

[31]

[35]

[36]

[33]

[34]

[37]

[38]

[39]

[42]

[43]

[40]

[41]

[44]

[45]

[47]

[48]

[46]

[49]

[50]